Contents

Meet the Marvels! 2

Captain Marvel Meets
the Metal Monster................................ 8

In this comic ...

Billy

Little sis

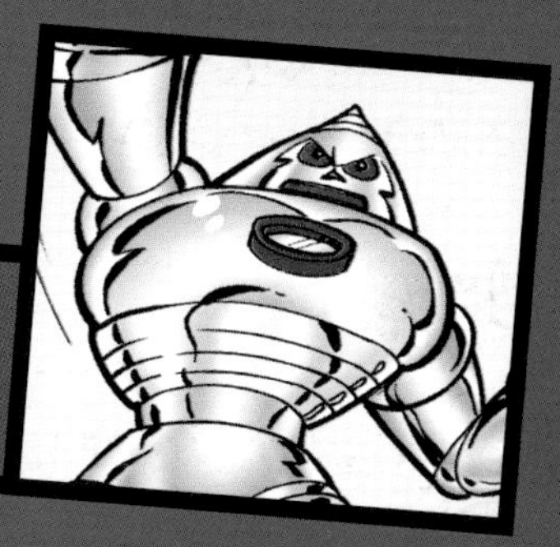

Metal Monster

Meet the Marvels!

Billy and his little sister were normal kids.

Then they met a wizard called Shazam.

Billy had lots of fun as Captain Marvel.

All safe and sound!
Take us up to the clouds!
Again! Again!
Sorry! I have too many jobs to do!
SHAZAM!
Krakout!
Billy was back to normal.

Billy was a television reporter.
Have you got any hot choc?
Enjoy it!
Morning!
MR MORRIS
I am a top reporter!
Top reporter, hey?
We will see.
Go out and find a good story, boy!

Just then ...
Kapoy!
Crash!
Boom!
Shatter!
A metal monster!
You have just found
a story, Billy!

Thanks, little sis.

Crash!
That was close!

You are so brave!

Just doing my job!

Come on, little sis!

Oh no! Look!
The monster was back!

The metal monster took hold of Captain Marvel!

I will get you out!

Turn the monster off!

Found it!

Click!

There was a loud sound.
The metal monster blew up.

I am proud of you, little sis!

Hooray!

Thank you, Captain Marvel!
Any time! Just doing my job!